The Fourth
WISE MAN

By Mig Holder
Illustrated by Tony Morris

Long, long ago and far, far away there stood a
beautiful pillared house. Every cool, pale room was
lined with marble and hung with silk and satin.
This house belonged to a young man called Artaban. He
stood at an upper window with three friends, gazing out at
the night sky. They were Wise Men, who spent their time
studying the stars and reading ancient books of their land.
'There it is!' cried Melchior, one of the Wise Men, pointing
excitedly. They all looked. There in the sky was the
brightest star they had ever seen.
The other two, Caspar and Balthazar, spread out a long
parchment scroll.
'It's just as the old writings tell,' they said wonderingly. 'If
we follow that star, we shall find a baby king who will
grow up to change the world!'

4

The three older men, Caspar, Melchior and Balthazar, at once started to make plans.

'We must follow the star and find the king!'

'We will need food, maps and new camels.'

'How soon can we leave?'

They seemed to forget that Artaban was there at all.

'Where shall I meet you?' he asked quietly.

The others turned and looked at him.

'No need for you to come,' said Melchior.

'But I want nothing more in all the world,' said Artaban. 'I have the strangest feeling that, if I follow the star, I shall find not only a new king but the secrets of life.'

The three Wise Men stared at Artaban as if he were mad. Finally Caspar's eyes lit up nastily,

'All right, Artaban,' he said. 'We will go to the Temple of the Seven Spheres, at Borsippa, where we store our charts and instruments. We will wait there three days. But if you are not there by midnight on the third day we will leave without you.'

'Oh thank you, thank you,' said Artaban, and hurtled off to get ready.

'But we don't want him stringing along,' complained Balthazar.

'Why do you think I said meet at the temple?' replied Caspar. 'You know how hopeless he is; he'll never make it!'

And they all roared with laughter.

6

ARTABAN was terribly excited; he couldn't wait to set off on his journey. But there was so much to do. He needed cool clothes for the day, warm clothes at night, a tent, blankets, food for himself, food for the camel, bottles of water, flagons of oil... The list grew and grew! What else? Of course! A present for the baby king!

Rushing from the house, Artaban made his way to the market square, where all the rich men gathered. Not hesitating for a moment, he sold all his possessions: his books, his furniture, his beautiful house, and all but one of his camels. With the money he bought three priceless jewels - the bluest sapphire, the reddest ruby and the snowiest pearl you have ever seen.

'Fit for a king,' he whispered, as he wrapped them tightly into a little leather pouch which he tucked into his belt.

As soon as the first rays of sun came glinting over the white town next morning Artaban was ready to go. He had been up all night folding and refolding, trying to squeeze all his belongings into two saddle bags. Finally he hoisted himself up onto the camel's back and was off!

For two days all went well. The air was clear and cool; the camel was fresh and ran smoothly over the desert sands. When the sun became too hot, they rested in the shade of rocks; when it grew dark, Artaban pitched his little tent and slept.

On the third day the path became steeper and rougher, the sun seemed hotter than ever, and the camel was tiring. But Artaban dare not stop to rest; he might not reach the temple in time! He urged the camel onwards.

Suddenly, from somewhere just off the road there came a moan. Artaban stopped in his tracks. There it was again!

Very unwillingly, Artaban climbed down from the camel.
Huddled behind a rock was the twisted figure of a man. He
had a gash on his head and his eyes were drooping shut.
Artaban hesitated. If he stopped to help, he would never reach
the temple in time.
The injured man stretched out a feeble hand,
'I've been robbed,' he whispered. 'Help me!'

In that moment Artaban made up his mind. He knew the three Wise Men would leave without him. Sighing to himself, he tipped out a little of his precious water, washed the man's wound and bandaged it with a strip of cloth. Then he heaved the injured man up onto his camel's back and set off at a snail's pace towards the last village he had passed.

It was nearly dark when they reached the village. Tired as he was, Artaban trudged from door to door, begging someone to look after the injured man. But at every house it was the same question: 'Who's going to pay for his food and medicine?' As the door of the next house creaked open, Artaban held out his sparkling sapphire.

'Will you look after this poor man for me?' The astonished woman nodded, her hand closing over the jewel as she led the man inside.

That night, while he was making a fire to cook his supper, Artaban thought sadly of the other three Wise Men. It would soon be midnight; they would leave without him.

Suddenly he laughed out loud.

'Then I will go by myself!' he shouted out into the dark. 'I will follow the star until I find the secrets of life!'

14

And so he did. He slept by day and travelled at night, guided only by the bright star in the east. Weeks and months went by like this until, one dark night, Artaban felt sure the star had stopped moving. This must be the place where the baby king had been born!

16

He led his camel quietly into the sleepy village, and almost at once heard the sound of a baby crying in a nearby cottage. Could this be the end of his quest? He knocked loudly on the door. It opened just a crack; he glimpsed the tear-stained face of a terrified woman.

'Oh, you're not a soldier!' she gasped in relief.

'No, just a weary traveller,' said Artaban, and he explained his journey.

'You'd better come in,' said the woman quietly, opening the door.

In the corner of the dark room a man was doing his best to hush the crying baby.

'We're so afraid,' said the woman. 'There was a baby born here in Bethlehem. They called him Jesus - maybe he's the baby you're looking for. Someone said he would grow up to be a king. Anyway - the real king, King Herod, got angry and ordered every baby boy under two years old to be killed. That's why we're so frightened each time there's a knock at the door.'

At that moment there came the sound of boots marching down the street. The woman gasped in terror and the baby set up a wail.

Then came a loud rap on the door.

Artaban thought very fast. With one hand on his belt he opened the door and stepped outside. He came face to face with a soldier brandishing a very sharp sword.

The soldier tried to shove Artaban aside.

'Let me pass - there's a child in here!'

But Artaban silently stretched out his hand to the soldier; in his fingers lay the red, red ruby, sparkling in the moonlight.

'If I give you this, will you go away and not harm the baby?'

Without another word, the soldier took the jewel and went on up the street.

'How can we ever thank you?' cried the baby's mother. She had seen everything through a crack in the door. 'That ruby was priceless!'

'Nothing is more valuable than the life of a child,' said Artaban, quietly letting himself out of the house.

Artaban climbed back on his camel. He was downhearted; not only was he no nearer to finding the secrets of life, but now he had given away two of the precious jewels that were supposed to be presents for the baby king.

So Artaban journeyed on. Someone told him the baby king might be in the land of Egypt, where his parents had fled with him to escape the soldiers. But Artaban could find no trace of them there.
He began to lose heart. Weeks turned to months, and months to years. Artaban travelled the world. But, tied to his belt, there was always one gem, a priceless pearl which he would never sell to anyone.

The one day, more than thirty years later, when he was quite an old man, Artaban found himself in the city of Jerusalem. It was festival time, and he strolled the sunny streets, enjoying the music and laughter.

Suddenly he came upon something horrible. A girl stood weeping, her hands tied behind her back. A man was poking at her and jeering, 'Who'll buy this one then? She'll make a hard-working slave.'

Artaban could not bear what he saw. He stepped forward.

'I will pay whatever you ask,' he said.

'With what?' sneered the man.

Artaban flushed. He had no money left in his pockets. Then his fingers brushed against the long-treasured pearl at his belt. With only a moment's hesitation, he held out the snow-white jewel. The crowd fell silent. That pearl was worth a hundred times the price of a slave! The trader grabbed it then shoved the girl roughly towards Artaban. He gently untied the girl's wrists.

'You're free to go,' he said.

She looked at him in disbelief.

'But you spent that beautiful pearl!'

'Freedom is worth more than a treasure chest of jewels,' said Artaban.

26

The next moment an angry mob surged up the street, parting Artaban from the girl. Men were shaking sticks and yelling, 'Jesus! Jesus! King of the Jews!'

Artaban stepped aside to let them past, and saw in horror that, right in the middle of the crowd, a man was being dragged along. A crown made from thorns was crammed onto his head and his face was bleeding.

Artaban knew then, without a doubt, that this was the man he had been seeking!

Seized with disappointment, Artaban missed his step and stumbled backwards. At once he felt a steadying hand on his arm. He looked up into a kind, smiling face.

'It's all wasted,' he muttered. 'I thought he would become a great king. But now it looks as though they're going to kill him.'

The woman didn't understand.

'Tell me,' she said gently.

'Many years ago,' Artaban began, 'I had three jewels... '

The woman listened quietly while he told her his long story. When he had finished, she said, 'I think your treasures were well spent.

Nothing is more valuable than a man's health, a child's life, a woman's freedom.'

Artaban turned his sad old face towards her. She laid her hand gently over his.

'I think that in searching for him, you have discovered the secrets of life!'

Then the King will say to those on his right, 'Come, you who are blessed by my Father, take your inheritance, the kingdom prepared for you since the creation of the world. For I was hungry and you gave me something to eat, I was thirsty and you gave me something to drink, I was a stranger and you invited me in, I needed clothes and you clothed me, I was sick and you looked after me, I was in prison and you came to visit me.'
Matthew 25:34–36